Inglés sin Barreras®

El Video-Maestro de Inglés Conversacional

10 Conversación informal

Cuaderno de ejercicios

Para información sobre
Inglés sin Barreras
en oferta especial de
Referido Preferido
1-800-305-6472
Dé el Código 03429

ISBN: 1-59172-312-4
ISBN: 978-1-59172-312-7

I705WB10

Índice

Lección uno

Vocabulario 5

Clase 8

Diálogo 10

Examen 11

Respuestas 12

Lección dos

Vocabulario 17

Clase 19

Diálogo 21

Examen 22

Respuestas 23

Lección tres

Vocabulario 27

Clase 29

Diálogo 32

Examen 33

Respuestas 34

Lección cuatro

Clase 39

Aprendamos viajando...............................45

Aprendamos conversando..........................51

Examen final 61

No se olvide de estudiar las lecciones en el manual antes de hacer los ejercicios de este cuaderno.

Examen inicial

Antes de comenzar el estudio de este volumen, dedique unos minutos a contestar a las 15 preguntas del examen siguiente. Llene el círculo correspondiente a la respuesta correcta.

1. *They asked me about my _____.*
   O a) half time
   O b) supervise
   O c) original
   O d) instance
   O e) qualifications

2. *Have you _____ the Thanksgiving Day Parade?*
   O a) saw
   O b) never saw
   O c) ever seen
   O d) didn't see
   O e) see

3. *Have you ever _ her a promotion?*
   O a) given
   O b) gave
   O c) got
   O d) get
   O e) done

4. *Have your parents seen you __?*
   O a) ever
   O b) never
   O c) yesterday
   O d) recently
   O e) at 8:00

5. *_____ they ride the bus to school yesterday?*
   O a) When
   O b) Did
   O c) How
   O d) Have
   O e) Do

6. *All employees are _____ one coffee break each morning.*
   O a) allow
   O b) give
   O c) allowed
   O d) have
   O e) participate

7. *I _____ go on Saturday if I don't have to work.*
   O a) maybe
   O b) definite
   O c) ever
   O d) might
   O e) didn't

8. *She has _____ to Japan.*
   O a) never been
   O b) going
   O c) not going
   O d) ever gone
   O e) done

9. *I worked until midnight. You __.*
   O a) aren't tired
   O b) might be angry
   O c) should be cold
   O d) has to be angry
   O e) must be tired

10. *She always _____ for her mistakes.*
    O a) takes responsibility
    O b) participates
    O c) explains
    O d) co-workers
    O e) definite

11. *I can't _____ it. Is it smooth or rough?*
    O a) smell
    O b) taste
    O c) feel
    O d) hear
    O e) look

12. *Have you ever _____ a pink and yellow rose?*
    O a) heard
    O b) looks at
    O c) taste
    O d) feels
    O e) smelled

13. *He did it _____.*
    O a) with himself
    O b) with ourselves
    O c) by myself
    O d) by himself
    O e) with ourselves

14. *Is that Raúl's coat? No, it's ___.*
    O a) mine
    O b) her
    O c) not hers
    O d) their
    O e) not our

15. *Please bring my coat. _____ in the closet.*
    O a) Its
    O b) Mine
    O c) They're
    O d) It's
    O e) Theirs

Cuando haya estudiado todas las lecciones de este volumen, haga el mismo examen de nuevo. Lo encontrará al final de este cuaderno, en la página titulada "Examen final".

Compare los resultados obtenidos en este examen con los del examen final. Así comprobará lo que ha aprendido y podrá medir su progreso.

Cuando haya terminado este examen, empiece a estudiar la Lección uno.

Lección

1

1 Notas

Encontrará las respuestas en la página 12.

A. Escriba oraciones usando las palabras entre paréntesis.

Ejemplo: (relationship) _I have a good relationship with my boss._

1. (promotion) _____

   _____

2. (polite) _____

   _____

3. (qualifications) _____

   _____

4. (situation) _____

   _____

5. (explain) _____

   _____

6. (for instance) _____

   _____

Encontrará las respuestas en la página 12.

B. Resuelva el crucigrama.

Primero, complete las oraciones. Después, escriba las palabras que completan las oraciones en el cuadro siguiente, empezando por la casilla que lleva el número correspondiente.

Encontrará las respuestas en la página 12.

Horizontales

1. I asked my _____ for a promotion.

5. Have you ever _____, or managed, other people?

7. It's not easy to make _____.

9. Please be _____, not rude.

12. Now, _____ it's half time of the football game.

13. I don't understand. Can you _____?

Verticales

2. Be polite, not _____.

3. Please tell me your _____ for this job.

4. A good _____ with co-workers is important.

6. She's a _____ in the shoe department.

7. It was a difficult _____ when I asked for a promotion.

8. I waited inside _____ it rained.

10. This is the _____ contract, not a copy.

11. I need to _____ a break.

Encontrará las respuestas en la página 13.

C. Haga preguntas usando las palabras entre paréntesis.

Ejemplo: (you, see, a Mardi Gras Parade)

Have you ever seen a Mardi Gras Parade?

1. (they, visit, Toronto or Vancouver)

   _____

2. (she, walk, to school)

   _____

3. (Mr. Thomas, be, late to work)

   _____

4. (you, get, promotion)

   _____

5. (he, study, French)

   _____

6. (your family, eat, sushi)

   _____

7. (Mrs. Douglas, write, a letter to you)

   _____

8. (you, go, skiing at night)

   _____

Encontrará las respuestas en la página 13.

D. Escriba preguntas usando las palabras entre paréntesis. Fíjese en las expresiones de tiempo antes de escribir las preguntas.

Ejemplo: (go, school, yesterday) Did you go to school yesterday?

(go, a movie, recently) Have you gone to a movie recently?

(go, Australia) Have you ever gone to Australia?

1. (eat, breakfast, yet)

   _____

2. (watch TV, last night)

   _____

3. (see, a kangaroo)

   _____

4. (go on vacation, in July)

   _____

5. (play, the piano)

   _____

6. (listen to music, last night)

   _____

7. (talk on the phone, all night)

   _____

8. (study for the test, already)

   _____

Encontrará las respuestas en la página 14.

Decida si estos temas de conversación son personales o impersonales. Los temas personales son los que se pueden discutir únicamente con amigos cercanos y familiares.

health	~~personal~~	impersonal
family relationships	personal	impersonal
magazine stories	personal	impersonal
education	personal	impersonal
weather	personal	impersonal
salary	personal	impersonal
religion	personal	impersonal
movies	personal	impersonal
sports	personal	impersonal
appearance	personal	impersonal
politics	personal	impersonal
money	personal	impersonal
bus and train schedules	personal	impersonal
TV shows	personal	impersonal

Encontrará las respuestas en la página 14.

Haga un círculo alrededor de la palabra correcta.

Dear Mary,

How are you? I (have been / had been) on vacation from school (from / for) ten days. Tomorrow I (went / have to go) back to school. Last night I (go / went) with my friend, Calista, to (have seen / see) a movie, *The Mall*. It (was / were) very funny. (Are you seeing / Have you seen) it? I (was / have) also been shopping a little. I (to get / got) a promotion at work so I have some extra money. I (needed / needing) to buy some new shoes and a new coat. I (found / will find) a really cute green coat. I bought two pair of shoes! My boyfriend, Keith, (won't buy / bought) a new CD player. He also got some new CDs. He (likes / liking) jazz music. Have you ever (hears / heard) of Lew Mavis? He's great. (Will write / Write) to me soon. (I'll / I) see you in December.

Best wishes, Sandy

Vocabulario

A. Estas respuestas no son las únicas respuestas correctas.

1. I asked my boss for a promotion.
2. She was very polite.
3. My qualifications are good for this job.
4. It was a difficult situation.
5. Can you explain the company benefits?
6. He is always late. For instance, today he arrived at 9:45.

B.

					M	A	N	A	G	E	R		
											U		
			Q		R						D		
		S	U	P	E	R	V	I	S	E	D		
	S		A		L								
S	M	A	L	L	T	A	L	K					W
I	L		I		T								H
T	E		F		I								I
U	S		I		O								L
A	P		C		N		P	O	L	I	T	E	
T	E		A		S			R			A		
I	R		T		H			I			K		
O	S		I		I	M	A	G	I	N	E		
N	O		O		P			I					
	N		N					N					
			E	X	P	L	A	I	N				
								L					

Clase

C.
1. Have they ever visited Toronto or Vancouver?
2. Has she ever walked to school?
3. Has Mr. Thomas ever been late to work?
4. Have you ever gotten a promotion?
5. Has he ever studied French?
6. Has your family ever eaten sushi?
7. Has Mrs. Douglas ever written a letter to you?
8. Have you ever gone skiing at night?

D.
1. Have you eaten breakfast yet?
2. Did you watch TV last night?
3. Have you ever seen a kangaroo? (*or* Did you see a kangaroo?)
4. Did you go on vacation in July?
5. Have you ever played the piano? (*or* Did you play the piano?)
6. Did you listen to music last night?
7. Have you ever talked on the phone all night?
   (*or* Did you talk on the phone all night?)
8. Have you studied for the test already?

Diálogo

Las respuestas siguientes no son las únicas respuestas válidas. Este ejercicio da pié a otras alternativas que dependen en gran parte del criterio de cada persona.

health	⟨personal⟩	impersonal
family relationships	⟨personal⟩	impersonal
magazine stories	personal	⟨impersonal⟩
education	⟨personal⟩	impersonal
weather	personal	⟨impersonal⟩
salary	⟨personal⟩	impersonal
religion	⟨personal⟩	impersonal
movies	personal	⟨impersonal⟩
sports	personal	⟨impersonal⟩
appearance	⟨personal⟩	impersonal
politics	⟨personal⟩	impersonal
money	⟨personal⟩	impersonal
bus and train schedules	personal	⟨impersonal⟩
TV shows	personal	⟨impersonal⟩

Examen

How are you? I <u>have been</u> on vacation from school <u>for</u> ten days. Tomorrow I <u>have to go</u> back to school. Last night I <u>went</u> with my friend, Calista, to <u>see</u> a movie, *The Mall*. It <u>was</u> very funny. <u>Have you seen</u> it? I <u>have</u> also been shopping a little. I <u>got</u> a promotion at work so I have some extra money. I <u>needed</u> to buy some new shoes and a new coat. I <u>found</u> a really cute green coat. I <u>bought</u> two pair of shoes! My boyfriend, Keith, <u>bought</u> a new CD player. He also got some new CDs. He <u>likes</u> jazz music. Have you ever <u>heard</u> of Lew Mavis? He's great. <u>Write</u> to me soon. <u>I'll</u> see you in December.
Best wishes, Sandy

Lección

2

Encontrará las respuestas en la página 23.

A. Llene los espacios en blanco con las palabras de la lista siguiente.

appointment	participate	religion	allow
politics	co-workers	definite	workplace
might	must be	improve	get back to

Ejemplo: I ___*might*___ go on Saturday. I'm not sure.

1.   How can we _____ our English?

2.   He _____ there at 9:00 or he won't be able to take the test.

3.   _____ and _____ can be dangerous topics at work.

4.   She doesn't like to _____ in small talk at work.

5.   My managers _____ one coffee break in the morning.

6.   Be on time for your _____.

7.   I don't like to gossip with _____.

8.   We have a very pleasant _____.

9.   We should _____ work.

10.   Is your decision _____?

Encontrará las respuestas en la página 23.

B. Escriba oraciones que incluyan las palabras entre paréntesis.

Ejemplo: (I, never, see, a helicopter)

I have never seen a helicopter.

1. (Mr. Johnson, has, ever, allow, coffee breaks)

   _____

2. (Kelly, never, participate in, gossip)

   _____

3. (my co-workers, never, eat lunch in the office)

   _____

4. (you, have, ever, explain, your qualifications)

   _____

5. (he, never, make small talk)

   _____

6. (they, ever, go on, a business trip)

   _____

7. (she, never, take responsibility)

   _____

8. (you, have, ever, imagine, the perfect vacation)

   _____

Encontrará las respuestas en la página 23.

C. Seleccione la respuesta apropiada para cada una de las oraciones.

~~You must be tired.~~
He must not be Italian.
You must love Mexican food.
You must be hungry.
You must be crazy.

It must have been expensive.
She must miss them.
They must have been late.
She must be short.

Ejemplo: I went to sleep at midnight.

You must be tired.

1. The bus came at 9:30 not 9:00.

   _____

2. He spent all of his money on his new car.

   _____

3. We eat there 3 or 4 times a week!

   _____

4. Mary can't reach the drawer.

   _____

5. I told my boss that I will work every Saturday.

   _____

6. She hasn't seen her parents for ten months.

   _____

7. I didn't eat breakfast or lunch.

   _____

8. Tony hates spaghetti.

   _____

Encontrará las respuestas en la página 24.

D. Conteste a las preguntas usando las palabras entre paréntesis.

Ejemplo: Can you meet us Thursday at 6:00 PM?

(cannot) _____ *I can't.* _____

1.   Will you study for the test tonight.

(might) _____

2.   Is he going to be on time?

(should) _____

3.   Should we eat Italian food?

(could) _____

4.   Should I fill out the application?

(must) _____

5.   Are they qualified?

(might) _____

6.   Are you going to explain it to me?

(could) _____

7.   Will Mr. White be at the interview?

(might) _____

8.   Can we talk about the problem during the meeting?

(should) _____

9.   Will he be the new manager.

(might) _____

10. Is she definite about the time?

(must) _____

Encontrará las respuestas en la página 24.

Determine si los temas de conversación indicados pueden discutirse con las distintas personas que encabezan las columnas. Si el tema de conversación es apropiado, escriba las letras OK; si es cuestionable, escriba la letra C; si es demasiado personal, escriba las letras DP.

	with friends	with your boss	with your sister	at the bus stop
weather				
health				
salary				
religion				
politics				
TV shows				
a movie				
vacation plans				
children				
problem neighbor				
dept. store sale				

Encontrará las respuestas en la página 24.

Lea el texto siguiente. Luego haga un círculo alrededor de la palabra más apropiada en cada oración.

We have a nice workplace. Everything is new including the cafeteria. The managers at the company are fair to all the employees, and the company has good benefits. Most of my co-workers are qualified for their jobs so it is easy to get things done. There isn't a lot of gossip in the office, but we do make small talk in the hallways. I have made some good friends at the company.

1. He <u>would / wouldn't</u> look for a another job right away.

2. He <u>can / can't</u> talk to his co-workers in the hallway.

3. The company <u>might / might not</u> be a good place to fill out an application.

4. The employees <u>must / must not</u> eat in the cafeteria most of the time.

5. The managers <u>should / shouldn't</u> be criticized for being unfair.

6. The employees <u>can / can't</u> do their jobs easily.

7. The employees <u>must / must not</u> complain about their jobs a lot.

8. This <u>could / couldn't</u> be the perfect company.

Vocabulario

A.
1. improve
2. must be
3. Religion and politics
4. participate
5. allow
6. appointment
7. co-workers
8. workplace
9. get back to
10. definite

B.
1. Has Mr. Johnson ever allowed coffee breaks?
2. Kelly never participates in gossip.
3. My co-workers never eat lunch in the office.
4. Have you ever explained your qualifications?
5. He never makes small talk.
6. Have they ever gone on a business trip?
7. She never takes responsibility.
8. Have you ever imagined the perfect vacation?

Clase

C.
1. They must have been late.
2. It must have been expensive.
3. You must love Mexican food.
4. She must be short.
5. You must be crazy.
6. She must miss them.
7. You must be hungry.
8. He must not be Italian.

D.
1. I might.
2. He should be.
3. We could.
4. You must.
5. They might be.
6. I could.
7. He might be.
8. We should.
9. He might be.
10. She must be.

Diálogo

Answers will vary.

Examen

1. wouldn't
2. can
3. might
4. must
5. shouldn't
6. can
7. must not
8. could

Lección

3

Encontrará las respuestas en la página 34.

A. Reemplace los nombres entre paréntesis por pronombres.

Ejemplo: (My brother) _____*He*_____ sent me a birthday card.

1. Leslie sent (Mrs. Martin) _____ an invitation.

2. They ate (my sandwich) _____.

3. I can't find (the newspaper) _____.

4. (My co-workers) _____ are allowed one coffee break.

5. (The dog's) _____ tail is very short.

6. Please don't take (Paula's) _____ dictionary.

7. Is this (your bicycle) _____?

8. Paul wrote the poem by (Paul) _____.

Encontrará las respuestas en la página 34.

B. Sopa de letras
Encuentre las palabras de la lista siguiente en el cuadro de abajo. Las palabras se leen de izquierda a derecha y de arriba abajo.

agree, allow, avoid, bill, dangerous, delicious, demotion, explain, gossip, hers, imagine, indicate, itself, mine, opera, personal, politics, possible, promotion, qualification, rude, team, theirs, while, whisper

Q	U	A	L	I	F	I	C	A	T	I	O	N	B	I	L	L
D	E	L	I	C	I	O	U	S	T	E	A	M	X	N	G	D
G	R	L	N	P	T	E	X	P	L	A	I	N	C	D	P	A
O	U	O	P	E	R	A	H	E	D	E	M	O	T	I	O	N
S	D	W	H	I	S	P	E	R	O	A	A	P	H	C	L	G
S	E	I	T	S	E	L	F	S	U	V	G	N	E	A	I	E
I	P	R	O	M	O	T	I	O	N	O	I	H	I	T	T	R
P	O	S	S	I	B	L	E	N	M	I	N	E	R	E	I	O
T	A	K	E	A	B	R	E	A	K	D	E	R	S	L	C	U
A	G	R	E	E	W	H	I	L	E	A	R	S	W	D	S	S

Encontrará las respuestas en la página 35.

C. Llene los espacios en blanco con el verbo correcto.

Ejemplo: I can't _____*smell*_____ the flowers.

 1.   This orange _____ sour.

 2.   Does the paper _____ smooth or rough?

 3.   Does that car _____ new?

 4.   That bakery _____ wonderful.

 5.   He said he couldn't _____ the key under the seat.

Encontrará las respuestas en la página 35.

6. Did you _____ that loud music last night?

7. Did you _____ the movie on Saturday night?

8. He never _____ the soup while it's cooking.

9. Have you ever _____ a white tiger?

10. That _____ like a washing machine!

D. Llene los espacios en blanco con el pronombre correcto.

Ejemplo: (he) We met ___*him*___ at the movie theater.

1.   (she) Let's call _____ on Monday morning.

2.   (they) That car is _____.

3.   (I) _____ left _____ coat on the bus last night.

4.   (we) The doctor gave _____ the same prescription.

5.   (it) _____ fixed _____.

6.   (you) Is that _____ pen over there?

7.   (me, he) That's not _____, it's _____.

8.   (we) _____ cooked everything _____.

9.   (you) Is this _____?

10. (they, I) _____ walked to the bus stop with

   _____.

Encontrará las respuestas en la página 35.

Redacte una invitación para una fiesta. Describa la fiesta, precise cuándo y dónde se celebrará y proporcione los detalles adicionales que crea conveniente.

What: _____

_____

When: _____

_____

Where: _____

_____

Details: _____

_____

R.S.V.P. _____

_____

Encontrará las respuestas en la página 36.

Si es posible, reemplace las palabras subrayadas por pronombres.

Dear (1) <u>Anna and David</u>,

Thank you for inviting (2) <u>Randy and Kathy</u> for dinner. (3) <u>Randy and Kathy</u> are always happy to come to (4) <u>Anna and David's</u> house. (5) <u>Randy and Kathy</u> love the way (6) <u>David</u> cooks. The dishes (7) <u>David</u> prepares are always so tasty. I wish (8) <u>Randy</u> could cook that well!

(9) <u>Kathy is</u> the cook in (10) <u>Randy and Kathy's</u> house. (11) <u>My mother</u> gave (12) <u>Kathy</u> some wonderful recipes. But some of (13) <u>the recipes</u> are too difficult. (14) <u>The recipes</u> take too many ingredients and (15) <u>the dishes</u> never taste right.

Just the way (16) <u>Anna and David's</u> house smells when (17) <u>Randy and Kathy</u> come to dinner is wonderful. (18) <u>Randy and Kathy</u> know that (19) <u>Randy and Kathy</u> will always eat well. Why don't (20) <u>Anna and David</u> let (21) <u>Randy and Kathy</u> take (22) <u>Anna and David</u> to dinner next time (23) <u>Anna, David, Randy and Kathy</u> get together?

Thanks, again. Best wishes,

Kathy

Vocabulario

A.
1. her
2. mine
3. it
4. We
5. Its
6. her
7. yours
8. himself

B.

Clase

C.
1. tastes
2. feel
3. look
4. smells
5. feel
6. hear
7. see
8. tastes
9. seen
10. sounds

D.
1. her
2. theirs
3. I, my
4. us
5. It, itself
6. your
7. mine, his
8. We, ourselves
9. yours
10. They, me

Diálogo

Answers will vary.

Examen

1. Anna and David
2. us
3. We
4. your
5. We
6. David
7. he
8. Randy
9. I am
10. our
11. My mother
12. me
13. them
14. They
15. the dishes
16. your
17. we
18. We
19. we
20. you
21. us
22. you
23. we

Lección

4 Notas

Piense en lo que puede hacer para seguir aprendiendo inglés. Recuerde las palabras de la Sra. West: "Practique, practique, practique." En su calendario, anote las cosas que hará en inglés cada día. Empiece por describir diez formas de practicar inglés. Escriba también lo que va a necesitar para cumplir sus objetivos. Hemos incluido una idea como ejemplo.

1. If I see a word I don't understand, I will look it up in a dictionary. If I don't have a dictionary, I'll write it down and look it up later. Then, I'll make some sentences using the word.

2. _____

_____

_____

3. _____

_____

_____

4. _____

_____

_____

5. _____

_____

_____

6. _____

_____

_____

7. _____

_____

_____

8. _____

_____

_____

9. _____

_____

_____

10. _____

_____

_____

11. _____

_____

_____

12. _____

_____

_____

Les felicitamos por el esfuerzo realizado
y les deseamos mucha suerte.

Lección

V

Encontrará las respuestas en la página 47.

San Francisco

Antes de completar este ejercicio, vea la sección "Aprendamos viajando" incluida en el video y lea la misma sección en el manual.

Si la información contenida en la oración es verdadera, haga un círculo alrededor de la palabra *True*. Si la información es falsa, haga un círculo alrededor de la palabra *False* y escriba una oración con la información correcta.

True *False* 1. There is a famous mission in San Luis Obispo.

_____

True *False* 2. San Francisco is a very large city.

_____

True *False* 3. San Francisco is on the Atlantic Ocean.

_____

True *False* 4. San Francisco is famous for its skyline.

_____

True *False* 5. The Golden Gate Bridge is almost two miles long.

_____

True *False* 6. The Golden Gate Bridge was built in the 1920s.

_____

Encontrará las respuestas en la página 47.

True   *False*   7.   The technology used in gold mines was also used to build the cable car system.

_____

True   *False*   8.   Alcatraz is also known as "The Prison."

_____

True   *False*   9.   San Francisco's Chinatown has a Dragon's Gate.

_____

True   *False*   10.   The "summer of love" happened in the 1980s in the Haight-Ashbury section of the city.

_____

True   *False*   11.   "The Crookedest Street in the World" is Lombard Street.

_____

True   *False*   12.   Golden Gate Park has several famous museums.

_____

1. True.
2. False. It's a rather small city of one million people.
3. False. It's on the Pacific Ocean.
4. True.
5. True.
6. False. It was built in the 1930s.
7. True.
8. False. Alcatraz is known as "The Rock."
9. True.
10. False. The "summer of love" happened in the 1960s.
11. True.
12. True.

Lección

C

Encontrará las respuestas en la página 54.

Actividad 1. Opuestos: prefijos negativos
Escuche y cambie las oraciones.

in—

Most of your answers are _____.

You are too _____.

I like to wear _____ clothes.

im—

I believe that nothing is _____.

They were very _____.

That's so _____.

un—

That's why I'm so _____.

I've been _____ for a long time.

The staff here is very _____.

Actividad 2. Los deportes
Escoja la respuesta que se aplica a lo que a usted
le gusta o no le gusta.

I enjoy playing _____, and I enjoy watching it.

I don't enjoy playing _____, and I don't enjoy watching it.

I enjoy playing _____, but I don't enjoy watching it.

I don't enjoy playing _____, but I enjoy watching it.

Actividad 3. Posibilidades
Pida que le repitan lo que le acaban de decir.

Maybe ____'ll _____.

Maybe _____ won't _____.

_____ might _____.

_____ might not _____.

Actividad 4. Probabilidades
Exprese probabilidades basadas en la información que se da.

_____ must _____.

_____ must not _____.

Actividad 5. Diálogos
Escuche y siga las instrucciones que siguen.

Diálogo 1

I've _____.

Diálogo 2

I wanted to tell you that _____.

I forgot to tell you that _____.

I forgot to mention that _____.

Did I tell you that_____?

Did I mention that _____?

By the way, _____.

Encontrará las respuestas en la página 54.

Diálogo 3

Let me _____.

Diálogo 4

I've been _____ lately.

Actividad 6. I Walk the Line
Escuche.

Actividad 7. Pronombres posesivos
Use las formas posesivas alternativas.

Whose _____ is this?

It's my _____. It's mine.

It's your _____. It's yours.

It's his _____. It's his.

It's her _____. It's hers.

It's our _____. It's ours.

It's their _____. It's theirs.

Actividad 8. Las preguntas y el tiempo a que se refieren
Decida si las oraciones se refieren al presente, al pasado o al futuro, y haga las preguntas.

Actividad 1.

in—
Most of your answers are <u>incorrect</u>.
You are too <u>inexperienced</u>.
I like to wear <u>informal</u> clothes.

im—
I believe that nothing is <u>impossible</u>.
They were very <u>impolite</u>.
That's so <u>impractical</u>.

un—
That's why I'm so <u>unhappy</u>.
I've been <u>unemployed</u> for a long time.
The staff here is very <u>unfriendly</u>.

Actividad 7.

It's my <u>jacket</u>. It's mine.

It's your <u>desk</u>. It's yours.

It's his <u>bag</u>. It's his.

It's her <u>book</u>. It's hers.

It's our <u>car</u>. It's ours.

It's their <u>computer</u>. It's theirs.

Notas

Notas

Notas

Notas

Notas

Para información sobre
Inglés sin Barreras
en oferta especial de
Referido Preferido
1-800-305-6472
Dé el Código 03429

Llene el círculo correspondiente a la respuesta correcta.

1. They asked me about my _____.
- a) half time
- b) supervise
- c) original
- d) instance
- e) qualifications

2. Have you _____ the Thanksgiving Day Parade?
- a) saw
- b) never saw
- c) ever seen
- d) didn't see
- e) see

3. Have you ever _ her a promotion?
- a) given
- b) gave
- c) got
- d) get
- e) done

4. Have your parents seen you __?
- a) ever
- b) never
- c) yesterday
- d) recently
- e) at 8:00

5. _____ they ride the bus to school yesterday?
- a) When
- b) Did
- c) How
- d) Have
- e) Do

6. All employees are _____ one coffee break each morning.
- a) allow
- b) give
- c) allowed
- d) have
- e) participate

7. I _____ go on Saturday if I don't have to work.
- a) maybe
- b) definite
- c) ever
- d) might
- e) didn't

8. She has _____ to Japan.
- a) never been
- b) going
- c) not going
- d) ever gone
- e) done

9. I worked until midnight. You __.
- a) aren't tired
- b) might be angry
- c) should be cold
- d) has to be angry
- e) must be tired

10. She always _____ for her mistakes.
- a) takes responsibility
- b) participates
- c) explains
- d) co-workers
- e) definite

11. I can't _____ it. Is it smooth or rough?
- a) smell
- b) taste
- c) feel
- d) hear
- e) look

12. Have you ever _____ a pink and yellow rose?
- a) heard
- b) looks at
- c) taste
- d) feels
- e) smelled

13. He did it _____.
- a) with himself
- b) with ourselves
- c) by myself
- d) by himself
- e) with ourselves

14. Is that Raúl's coat? No, it's ___.
- a) mine
- b) her
- c) not hers
- d) their
- e) not our

15. Please bring my coat. _____ in the closet.
- a) Its
- b) Mine
- c) They're
- d) It's
- e) Theirs

Cuando termine el examen, llame a Profesores al (800) 788-8303 para contestarlo y un profesor lo asesore en su pronunciación y avance.

Si lo prefiere, corte el examen en la línea de puntos y envíelo a:
Profesores
6380 Wilshire Blvd
Suite 1400
Los Angeles, CA
90048

Por favor, escriba claramente su nombre y dirección (use tinta oscura) para que podamos enviarle el examen corregido.

Nombre _____
Dirección _____
Ciudad _____ Estado _____
Código Postal _____ País _____

Si desea saber las respuestas de una forma inmediata, visite nuestra página Web, www.isbonline.com y haga el examen en el Internet.

Si desea enviar sus exámenes por correo electrónico o hacernos alguna pregunta, escríbanos a: profesores@isbonline.com

Fecha _____
Nº. de contrato _____
Teléfono (_____) _____

Felicitaciones por haber alcanzado el último examen escrito, pero aún queda bastante por hacer. Cuando haya terminado de estudiar el resto del curso, envíenos un fax o escríbanos para solicitar un examen oral.

Respuestas

1. (e) qualifications
2. (c) ever seen
3. (a) given
4. (d) recently
5. (e) Do
6. (c) allowed
7. (d) might
8. (a) never been
9. (e) must be tired
10. (a) takes responsibility
11. (c) feel
12. (e) smelled
13. (d) by himself
14. (a) mine
15. (d) It's

- promotion
- qualifications
- situation

- Keep me posted.
- I don't think so.
- Take a guess.

- workplace
- business trip
- co-worker
- team

- (to) improve
- (to) avoid
- (to) allow

- I have never eaten sushi.
- She has never eaten sushi.

- She's not here today. She must be sick.
- He must have seen this movie.

- Will he be home?
- He might be.
- Can you be home by 11:00 PM?
- I should be.

- dangerous, safe
- qualified, unqualified
- demotion

- responsible, irresponsible
- enjoyable, unenjoyable

- I forgot.
- I'd rather not say.
- I'm not sure.

- bill
- curious
- It won't take long.

- This book is mine.
- This coat is hers.

- I wrote this report myself.
- He did everything himself.

- It smells good.
- It feels smooth.
- It sounds awful.

- (to) date
- (to) invite
- (to) interrupt

- formal
- informal
- personal
- impersonal

- (to) congratulate
- (to) imagine

- (to) keep a close watch
- (to) supervise

- lugar de trabajo
- viaje de negocios
- compañero(a) de trabajo
- equipo

- Manténme informado.
- No creo.
- Adivina.

- ascenso
- calificaciones
- situación

- Ella no está aquí hoy. Debe de estar enferma.
- Él debe de haber visto esta película.

- Nunca he comido sushi.
- Ella nunca ha comido sushi.

- mejorar
- evitar
- permitir

- responsable, irresponsable
- agradable, desagradable

- peligroso(a), seguro(a)
- competente, incompetente
- descenso

- ¿Estará él en casa?
- Puede que sí.
- ¿Puedes llegar a casa antes de las once?
- Debería poder hacerlo.

- Este libro es mío.
- Este abrigo es de ella.

- factura
- curioso(a)
- No tomará mucho tiempo.

- Lo olvidé.
- Preferiría no comentar.
- No estoy seguro.

- salir con alguien
- invitar
- interrumpir

- Huele bien.
- Es suave al tacto.
- Suena horrible.

- Escribí este informe yo mismo.
- El hizo todo solo.

- vigilar de cerca
- supervisar

- felicitar
- imaginar

- formal
- informal
- personal
- impersonal